Math Mammoth Grade 3 Tests and Cumulative Reviews

for the complete curriculum
(Canadian Version)

Includes consumable student copies of:

- Chapter Tests
- End-of-year Test
- Cumulative Reviews

By Maria Miller

Contents

4

Grade 3, Chapter 1

End-of-Chapter Test

Instructions to the student:

Answer each question in the space provided.

Instructions to the teacher:

My suggestion for grading the chapter 1 test is below. The total is 39 points. You can give partial points for partial solutions. Divide the student's score by the total of 39 to get a decimal number, and change that decimal to percent to get the student's percentage score. For example, if the student scores 25, divide 25 ÷ 39 with a calculator to get 0.6410256. The percent score is 64%.

Question #	Max. points	Student score
1	6 points	
2	3 points	
3	6 points	
4	3 points	
5	4 points	
6	4 points	

Question #	Max. points	Student score
7	4 points	
8	2 points	
9	3 points	
10	2 points	
11	2 points	
TOTAL	39 points	

Chapter 1 Test

1. Solve in your head and then write the answers.

a. $210 + 60 =$ _____ $198 + 5 =$ _____	**b.** $55 + 38 =$ _____ $99 + 30 =$ _____	**c.** $82 - 35 =$ _____ $880 - 9 =$ _____

2. Solve what number goes in place of the triangle.

a. $52 - \triangle = 47$ $\triangle =$ _____	**b.** $\triangle - 20 = 267$ $\triangle =$ _____	**c.** $693 + \triangle = 701$ $\triangle =$ _____

3. Write the Roman numerals using normal numbers.

a. IV	**b.** LXVI	**c.** LXXVIII
d. CXLIV	**e.** XXIX	**f.** XCVIII

4. Jamie has $250. He bought a camera for $127 and batteries for $18. How much money does he have left?

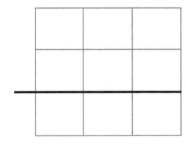 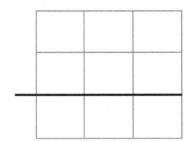

5. Subtract. *Check* the result of each subtraction by adding.

Check:	Check:
a. 4 0 4 $-$ 1 5 7 $+$	**b.** 7 2 3 $-$ 3 9 7 $+$

6. Round the numbers to the nearest ten.

a. 708 ≈ _____	**b.** 595 ≈ _____	**c.** 824 ≈ _____	**d.** 457 ≈ _____

7. Calculate.

a. $70 - 40 - 8 + 5 =$ _____	**c.** $(300 - 30) + (60 - 20) =$ _____
b. $70 - (40 - 8) + 5 =$ _____	**d.** $300 - 30 + (70 - 20) =$ _____

8. One year has 365 days. Of those, 206 are school days.
   How many days in a year are not school days?

9. Jay has four boxes of trading cards. Each
   of the boxes contains 80 cards, except
   the last box has 28 cards missing.
   How many trading cards does he have?

10. Fill in the
    missing parts.

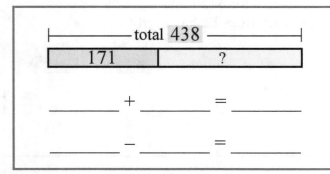
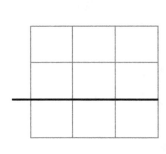

11. Solve.
    $609 - (169 + 145) =$ _____

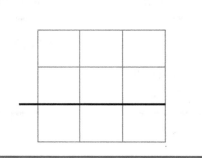

8

Grade 3, Chapter 2

End-of-Chapter Test

Instructions to the student:

Answer each question in the space provided.

Instructions to the teacher:

My suggestion for grading the chapter 2 test is below. The total is 26 points. You can give partial points for partial solutions. Divide the student's score by the total of 26 to get a decimal number, and change that decimal to percent to get the student's percentage score. For example, if the student scores 20, divide $20 \div 26$ with a calculator to get 0.7692307. The percent score is 77%.

Question #	Max. points	Student score
1	12 points	
2	4 points	

Question #	Max. points	Student score
3	6 points	
4	4 points	
Total	26 points	

Chapter 2 Test

1. Multiply.

a.	b.	c.	d.
$2 \times 3 = $ _____	$2 \times 5 = $ _____	$2 \times 20 = $ _____	$1 \times 9 = $ _____
$1 \times 5 = $ _____	$3 \times 10 = $ _____	$3 \times 40 = $ _____	$11 \times 0 = $ _____
$0 \times 7 = $ _____	$2 \times 6 = $ _____	$2 \times 200 = $ _____	$11 \times 1 = $ _____

2. Draw a picture to illustrate the problems.

a. 3×5	**b.** $2 \times 5 + 3 \times 4$

3. Write a number sentence for each problem and solve.

a. Each basket holds 12 apples.
How many apples are in three baskets?

b. Chloe bought four pens for \$2 each and two games for \$8 each.
What was the total bill?

c. If you make groups of 4 sticks, and you have 20 sticks,
how many groups can you make?

4. Calculate.

a. $5 + 3 \times 5$	**b.** $20 + 2 \times 3 - 4$
c. $0 \times (10 + 2) \times 3$	**d.** $(8 - 3) \times 1 + 6$

Grade 3, Chapter 3

End-of-Chapter Test

Instructions to the student:

Answer each question in the space provided.

Instructions to the teacher:

My suggestion for grading the chapter 3 test is below. The total is 53 points. You can give partial points for partial solutions. Divide the student's score by the total of 53 to get a decimal number, and change that decimal to percent to get the student's percentage score. For example, if the student scores 44, divide $44 \div 53$ with a calculator to get 0.8301886. The percent score is 83%.

Question #	Max. points	Student score
1	17 points	
2	4 points	

Question #	Max. points	Student score
3	8 points	
4	24 points	
Total	53 points	

Chapter 3 Test

1. Fill in the complete multiplication table!

×	0	1	2	3	4	5	6	7	8	9	10	11	12
0													
1													
2													
3													
4													
5													
6													
7													
8													
9													
10													
11													
12													

2. **a.** Which multiplication fact is both in the table of 3 and in the table of 8?

b. Which multiplication fact is both in the table of 9 and in the table of 7?

3. Solve the problems.

a. A pet store has 10 kittens for sale. Five of them cost $9 each and the rest cost $5 each. How much would all 10 kittens cost?

b. If one table can seat six people, how many tables do you need for 54 people who are coming to the restaurant?

c. Ann saw seven dogs, four cats, and twelve geese at the park. How many feet do the animals have in total?

d. A T-shirt costs $6. How many shirts can you buy with $48?

4. Find the missing factors.

a.	b.	c.	d.
_____ × 6 = 24	7 × _____ = 77	5 × _____ = 35	_____ × 3 = 27
_____ × 6 = 54	7 × _____ = 42	_____ × 5 = 20	_____ × 3 = 12
_____ × 6 = 36	7 × _____ = 14	5 × _____ = 55	_____ × 3 = 36

e.	f.	g.	h.
_____ × 11 = 66	_____ × 8 = 64	_____ × 4 = 24	_____ × 12 = 144
_____ × 11 = 121	_____ × 8 = 16	_____ × 4 = 36	_____ × 12 = 48
11 × _____ = 22	8 × _____ = 32	4 × _____ = 16	12 × _____ = 84

Grade 3, Chapter 4

End-of-Chapter Test

Instructions to the student:

Answer each question in the space provided.

Instructions to the teacher:

My suggestion for grading the chapter 4 test is below. The total is 22 points. Divide the student's score by the total of 22 to get a decimal number, and change that decimal to percent to get the student's percentage score.

Question #	Max. points	Student score
1	8 points	
2	4 points	
3	4 points	

Question #	Max. points	Student score
4	2 points	
5	2 points	
6	2 points	
Total	22 points	

Chapter 4 Test

1. Write the time the clock shows, and the time 10 minutes later.

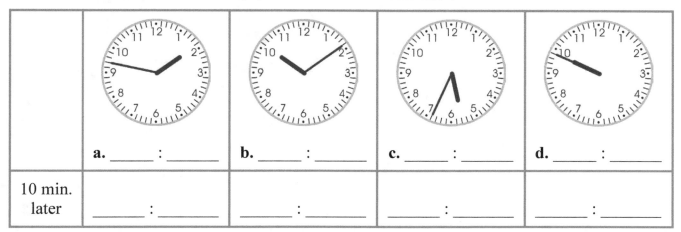

	a. _____ : _____	b. _____ : _____	c. _____ : _____	d. _____ : _____
10 min. later	_____ : _____	_____ : _____	_____ : _____	_____ : _____

2. How much time passes from the time on the clock till the next <u>full hour</u>?

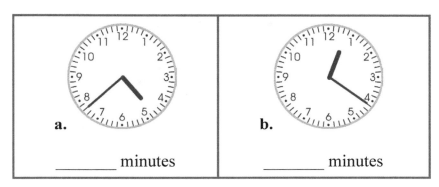

a. _____ minutes

b. _____ minutes

3. How much time passes?

a. from 4:13 till 6:13 _____ hours		**c.** from 3:10 till 3:53 _____ minutes
b. from 7:30 till 7:50 _____ minutes		**d.** from 11:26 till 12:00 _____ minutes

4. Denny left for the orchestra practice at 6:30 PM and arrived back home at 9:30 PM. How long was he gone?

5. A family left for a vacation on September 20, and returned two weeks later. On what date did they return?

September						
Sun	**Mon**	**Tue**	**Wed**	**Thu**	**Fri**	**Sat**
				1	2	3
4	5	6	7	8	9	10
11	12	13	14	15	16	17
18	19	20	21	22	23	24
25	26	27	28	29	30	

6. A soccer game started at 1:30 PM, and ended 50 minutes later. What time was it then?

Grade 3, Chapter 5

End-of-Chapter Test

Instructions to the student:

Answer each question in the space provided.

Instructions to the teacher:

My suggestion for grading the chapter 5 test is below. The total is 14 points. Divide the student's score by the total of 14 to get a decimal number, and change that decimal to percent to get the student's percentage score.

Question #	Max. points	Student score
1	2 points	
2	3 points	
3a	2 points	
3b	2 points	

Question #	Max. points	Student score
4a	2 points	
4b	2 points	
4c	1 points	
Total	14 points	

Chapter 5 Test

1. How much money? Write the amount.

   a. $_____

   b. $_____

2. Write as dollar amounts.

2 nickels, 3 dimes and 4 quarters	2 quarters, 6 dimes and 2 nickels	3 quarters, 4 dimes, and 1 nickel
a. $_____	**b.** $_____	**c.** $_____

3. Solve using mental maths.

   a. You bought stamps for $2.25, a pen for $0.75, and a notebook for $1.30. What was the total cost?

   b. What is your change from $5?

4. Solve.

a. Marsha has saved $25, and she wants to buy a game for $41.85. How much does she still need to save?

b. Mike bought a sandwich for $3.45,
soup for $2.25, juice for $1.65,
and water for $1.16.
Find the total cost.

c. Work out the change from $20.

Grade 3, Chapter 6

End-of-Chapter Test

Instructions to the student:

Answer each question in the space provided.

Instructions to the teacher:

My suggestion for grading the chapter 6 test is below. The total is 31 points. Divide the student's score by the total of 31 to get a decimal number, and change that decimal to percent to get the student's percentage score.

Question #	Max. points	Student score
1	4 points	
2	4 points	
3	4 points	

Question #	Max. points	Student score
4	3 points	
5	8 points	
6	8 points	
Total	31 points	

Chapter 6 Test

1. Write as normal numbers.

a. $2000 + 600 + 80 + 9 =$ _____	**b.** $70 + 4000 =$ _____
c. $600 + 9 + 5000 =$ _____	**d..** $3000 + 2 + 900 =$ _____

2. Compare, and write $<$, $>$ or $=$.

a. $600 + 40$ ☐ $400 + 60 + 1$ **b.** $200 + 7000$ ☐ $5000 + 800$

c. $700 + 5000$ ☐ $50 + 7000$ **d.** $900 + 8$ ☐ $8000 + 9$

3. Add and subtract in your head and write the answers.

a. $6300 +$ _____ $= 7000$	**b.** $5400 + 2700 =$ _____
$9700 - 1500 =$ _____	$9000 - 900 =$ _____

4. Round the numbers to the nearest hundred.

   a. $528 \approx$ _____   **b.** $1384 \approx$ _____   **c.** $2948 \approx$ _____

5. Add and subtract. <u>First</u> estimate by rounding.

a. Estimate: 2865 $+$ 4531 $\downarrow$ $\downarrow$ $+$ $=$ _____	**Calculate exactly:** 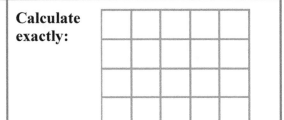
b. Estimate: 7002 $-$ 2973 $\downarrow$ $\downarrow$ $-$ $=$ _____	**Calculate exactly:** 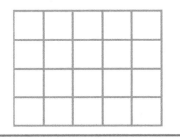

6. Solve.

a. An animal park buys animal feed for $1589 and tools for $325.
They pay with $2000. What is their change?

Also, estimate the answer
using rounded numbers.
My estimate:

_____

b. A new computer costs $2566 and a used one $650.
What is the price difference?

Also, estimate the answer using rounded numbers.

My estimate: _____

Grade 3, Chapter 7

End-of-Chapter Test

Instructions to the student:

Answer each question in the space provided.

Instructions to the teacher:

My suggestion for grading the chapter 7 test is below. The total is 38 points. Divide the student's score by the total of 38 to get a decimal number, and change that decimal to percent to get the student's percentage score.

Question #	Max. points	Student score
1	7 points	
2	2 points	
3	4 points	
4	4 points	

Question #	Max. points	Student score
5	5 points	
6	5 points	
7	4 points	
8	7 points	
Total	38 points	

Chapter 7 Test

1. Name any special quadrilaterals. If the quadrilateral does not have any special name, leave the line empty.

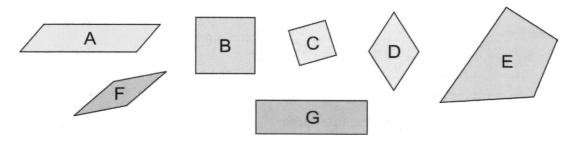

A _____

B _____

C _____

D _____

E _____

F _____

G _____

2. Find the area and perimeter of this figure.

   Area = _____

   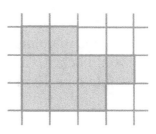

   Perimeter = _____

3. Solve. Write an addition with an unknown.

   The perimeter of this rectangle is 42 cm. Its one side is 14 cm. How long is the other side?

   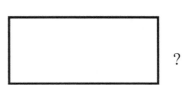

   _____

   Solution: ? = _____

4. Find the area and perimeter of these rectangles.

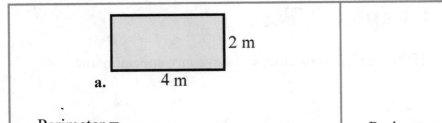

a.

Perimeter = _____

Area = _____

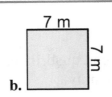

b.

Perimeter = _____

Area = _____

5. Write two multiplications to find the total area.

____ × ____ + ____ × ____ = _____

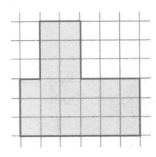

6. Margie's lawn is in the L-shape shown on the right. Calculate its area.

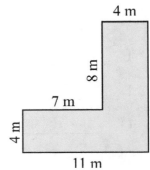

7. Jorge is planning to build a pen for his sheep. One possible pen would be a 16 m by 30 m rectangle, and the other possible pen would be a 12 m by 40 m rectangle.

Which pen has a larger perimeter? How much larger?

8. Write a number sentence for the total area, thinking of one rectangle or two.

____ × (____ + ____) = ____ × ____ + ____ × ____

area of the whole rectangle

area of the first part

area of the second part

Grade 3, Chapter 7

End-of-Chapter Test, Version 2

Instructions to the student:

Answer each question in the space provided.

Instructions to the teacher:

My suggestion for grading the chapter 7 test is below. The total is 38 points. Divide the student's score by the total of 38 to get a decimal number, and change that decimal to percent to get the student's percentage score.

Question	Max. points	Student score
1	7 points	
2	2 points	
3	4 points	
4	4 points	

Question	Max. points	Student score
5	5 points	
6	5 points	
7	4 points	
8	7 points	
Total	38 points	

Chapter 7 Test (Version 2)

1. Name any special quadrilaterals. If the quadrilateral does not have any special name, leave the line empty.

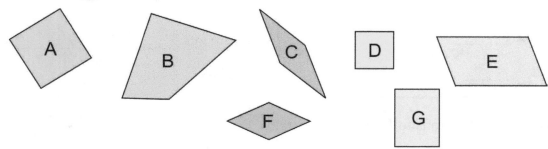

A _____

B _____

C _____

D _____

E _____

F _____

G _____

2. Find the area and perimeter of this figure.

Area = _____

Perimeter = _____

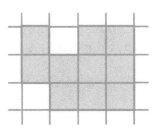

3. Solve. Write an addition with an unknown.

The perimeter of this rectangle is 108 cm. Its one side is 21 cm. How long is the other side?

_____

Solution: ? = _____

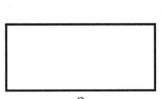

21 cm

?

4. Find the area and perimeter of these rectangles.

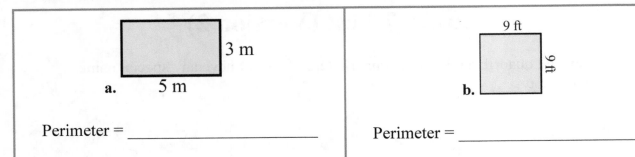

a. 3 m, 5 m

Perimeter = _____

Area = _____

b. 9 ft, 9 ft

Perimeter = _____

Area = _____

5. Write two multiplications to find the total area.

____ × ____ + ____ × ____ = _____

6. The floor of a building is in the L-shape shown on the right. Calculate its area.

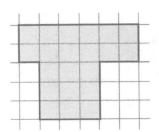

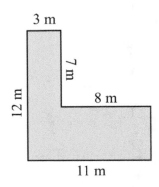

3 m

7 m

8 m

12 m

11 m

7. Lindsay has a rectangular 6 m by 7 m garden in her back yard. Her neighbour also has a garden, 4 m by 8 m.

Which garden has a larger perimeter?

How much larger?

8. Write a number sentence for the total area, thinking of one rectangle or two.

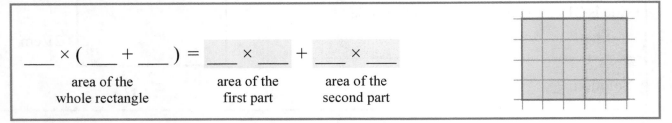

____ × (____ + ____) = ____ × ____ + ____ × ____

area of the whole rectangle

area of the first part

area of the second part

Grade 3, Chapter 8

End-of-Chapter Test

Instructions to the student:

Answer each question in the space provided.

Instructions to the teacher:

My suggestion for grading the chapter 8 test is below. The total is 20 points. Divide the student's score by the total of 20 to get a decimal number, and change that decimal to percent to get the student's percentage score.

Question #	Max. points	Student score
1	2 points	
2	2 points	
3	12 points	

Question #	Max. points	Student score
4	2 points	
5	2 points	
Total	20 points	

Chapter 8 Test

1. Draw lines of these lengths:

   a. 9 cm 5 mm

   b. 65 mm

2. Measure the sides of this triangle in millimetres.

3. Fill in each blank with a suitable unit. Sometimes several different units are possible

a. Mary's book weighed 350 _____ .	**d.** The recipe called for 200 _____ of flour.
b. A carton of juice had 2 _____ of juice.	**e.** Mom bought 3 _____ of bananas.
c. The airplane was flying 10 000 _____ above the ground.	**f.** Andrew and Ben rode their bicycles 10 _____ to the beach.
g. Erika weighs 55 _____ . **h.** The shampoo bottle can hold 450 ____ of shampoo. **i.** The large tank holds 200 ____ of water.	**j.** From Jack's house to the neighbour's is 50 _____ . **k.** A cell phone weighs 100 _____ . **l.** A housefly measured 17 _____ long.

4. Write the units in order from the smallest to the biggest unit: m km mm cm

5. Write the weights the scales are showing.

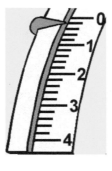
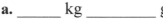

   a. _____ kg _____ g   **b.** _____ kg _____ g

Grade 3, Chapter 9

End-of-Chapter Test

Instructions to the student:

Answer each question in the space provided.

Instructions to the teacher:

My suggestion for grading the chapter 9 test is below. The total is 27 points. Divide the student's score by the total of 27 to get a decimal number, and change that decimal to percent to get the student's percentage score.

Question #	Max. points	Student score
1	6 points	
2	2 points	
3	8 points	

Question #	Max. points	Student score
4	3 points	
5	8 points	
Total	27 points	

Chapter 9 Test

1. For each multiplication, write two different division facts using the same numbers.

a. $6 \times 7 = $ _____	**b.** $5 \times 11 = $ _____
_____ ÷ _____ = _____	_____ ÷ _____ = _____
_____ ÷ _____ = _____	_____ ÷ _____ = _____

2. Draw a picture to illustrate the division $20 \div 4 = 5$.

3. Divide.

a.	b.	c.	d.
$48 \div 6 = $ _____	$99 \div 11 = $ _____	$49 \div 7 = $ _____	$0 \div 3 = $ _____
$12 \div 3 = $ _____	$70 \div 7 = $ _____	$54 \div 9 = $ _____	$18 \div 18 = $ _____

4. Divide and find the remainder.

a. $60 \div 8 = $ ____ R ____	**b.** $73 \div 10 = $ ____ R ____	**c.** $36 \div 5 = $ ____ R ____

5. Solve the problems.

a. Fifty-four children in first grade are arranged into groups of 6 for a trip. How many groups will they make?	**b.** The teacher bought 4 packages of six markers and 4 packages of ten markers. How many markers did she buy?
c. Ashley has 85 stickers. She puts them in a notebook, nine stickers on each page. How many pages *full* of stickers will she get?	**d.** Ashley tore three pages full of stickers off her notebook. How many stickers are on those pages?

Grade 3, Chapter 10

End-of-Chapter Test

Instructions to the student:

Answer each question in the space provided.

Instructions to the teacher:

My suggestion for grading the chapter 10 test is below. The total is 29 points. Divide the student's score by the total of 29 to get a decimal number, and change that decimal to percent to get the student's percentage score.

Question #	Max. points	Student score
1	4 points	
2	4 points	
3	4 points	
4	5 points	

Question #	Max. points	Student score
5	3 points	
6	3 points	
7	4 points	
8	2 points	
Total	29 points	

Chapter 10 Test

1. Compare the fractions, and write >, <, or = .

a. $\dfrac{8}{10}$ ☐ $\dfrac{9}{10}$ **b.** 1 ☐ $\dfrac{3}{7}$ **c.** $\dfrac{2}{3}$ ☐ $\dfrac{2}{5}$ **d.** $\dfrac{1}{2}$ ☐ $\dfrac{8}{9}$

2. Write these four fractions in order from the smallest to the largest:

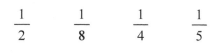
$\dfrac{1}{2}$ $\dfrac{1}{8}$ $\dfrac{1}{4}$ $\dfrac{1}{5}$

3. Divide the number line from 0 to 1 into equal parts. Then mark the fraction on it.

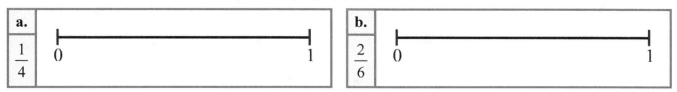

4. Mark the fractions and mixed numbers on the number line. $\dfrac{9}{5}$, $\dfrac{13}{5}$, $1\dfrac{1}{5}$, $2\dfrac{4}{5}$, $\dfrac{15}{5}$.

5. Write the whole numbers as fractions.

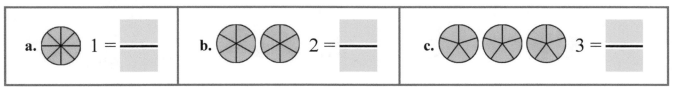

6. Write and shade the equivalent fractions.

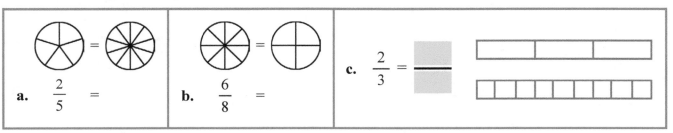

a. $\dfrac{2}{5} =$ **b.** $\dfrac{6}{8} =$ **c.** $\dfrac{2}{3} = \dfrac{}{}$

7. A loaf of bread is cut into 12 equal pieces.
   Another, similar loaf, is cut into 8 pieces.

   Mike ate 3 pieces of the first loaf.
   Janet ate 2 pieces of the second loaf.
   Who ate the greater amount of bread?

8. This picture is trying to show that $\dfrac{3}{9} = \dfrac{3}{8}$.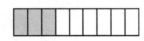

   Explain why it is wrong.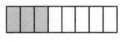

   $$\frac{3}{9} = \frac{3}{8}$$

48

Math Mammoth Grade 3 End-of-Year Test
International Version (Canada)

This test is quite long, so I do not recommend having your child/student do it in one sitting. Break it into parts and administer them either on consecutive days, or perhaps on morning/evening/morning. This is to be used as a diagnostic test. You may even skip those areas that you already know for sure your student has mastered.

The test does not cover every single concept that is covered in the *Math Mammoth Grade 3 Complete Curriculum*, but all the major concepts and ideas are tested here. This test is evaluating the child's ability in the following content areas:

- multiplication tables and basic division facts
- mental addition and subtraction
- regrouping in addition and subtraction
- basic word problems
- multiplication and related concepts
- clock to the minute and elapsed time calculations
- basic money calculations (finding totals and change)
- place value and rounding with four-digit numbers
- quadrilaterals, perimeter, and area
- division and related concepts (remainder, word problems)
- measuring lines in centimetres and millimetres
- basic usage of common metric measuring units
- the concept of a fraction and mixed number, equivalent fractions, and comparing fractions

Note 1: problems #2 and #3 are done <u>orally and timed</u>. Let the student see the problems. Read each problem aloud, and wait a maximum of 5-6 seconds for an answer. Mark the problem as right or wrong according to the student's (oral) answer. Mark it wrong if there is no answer. Then you can move on to the next problem.

You do not have to mention to the student that the problems are timed or that he/she will have 5-6 seconds per answer, because the idea here is not to create extra pressure by the fact it is timed, but simply to check if the student has the facts memorized (quick recall). You can say for example (vary as needed):

"I will ask you some multiplication and division questions. Try to answer me as quickly as possible. In each question, I will only wait a little while for you to answer, and if you do not say anything, I will move on to the next problem. So just try your best to answer the questions as quickly as you can."

In order to continue with the Math Mammoth Grade 4 Complete Curriculum, I recommend that the child gain a minimum score of 80% on this test, and that the teacher or parent review with him any content areas that are found weak. Children scoring between 70 and 80% may also continue with grade 4, depending on the types of errors (careless errors or not remembering something, vs. lack of understanding). The most important content areas to master are the multiplication tables and the word problems, because of the level of logical reasoning needed in them. Use your judgement.

Instructions to the student: Answer each question in the space provided.

Instructions to the teacher: See the grading grid below. The total is 207 points. A score of 166 points is 80%.

Grading on question 1 (the multiplication tables grid): There are 169 empty squares to fill in the table, and the completed table is worth 17 points. Count how many of the answers the student gets correct, divide that by 10, and round to the nearest whole point. For example: a student gets 24 correct: 24/10 = 2.4, which rounded becomes 2 points. Or, a student gets 85 correct: 85/10 = 8.5, which rounds to 9 points.

Question	Max. points	Student score
Multiplication Tables and Basic Division Facts		
1	17 points	
2	16 points	
3	16 points	
	subtotal	/ 49
Addition and Subtraction, Including Word Problems		
4	6 points	
5	6 points	
6	4 points	
7	4 points	
8	4 points	
9	3 points	
10	3 points	
11	4 points	
	subtotal	/ 34
Multiplication and Related Concepts		
12	1 point	
13	1 point	
14	3 points	
15	3 points	
16	1 point	
17	2 points	
18	1 point	
	subtotal	/ 12
Time		
19	8 points	
20	3 points	
	subtotal	/ 11

Question	Max. points	Student score
Graphs		
21a	1 point	
21b	1 point	
21c	1 point	
21d	2 points	
	subtotal	/ 5
Money		
22a	1 point	
22b	2 points	
22c	2 points	
23	2 points	
24	3 points	
	subtotal	/ 10
Place Value and Rounding		
25	2 points	
26	5 points	
27	4 points	
28	2 points	
29	8 points	
	subtotal	/ 21
Geometry		
30	5 points	
31	2 points	
32	4 points	
33	2 points	
34	2 points	
35	3 points	
	subtotal	/ 18

Question	Max. points	Student score
Measuring		
36	2 points	
37	2 points	
38	2 points	
39	6 points	
	subtotal	/ 12
Division and Related Concepts		
40	2 points	
41	6 points	
42	3 points	
43	2 points	
44	2 points	
	subtotal	/ 15
Fractions		
45	6 points	
46	3 points	
47	2 points	
48	3 points	
49	4 points	
50	2 points	
	subtotal	/ 20
	TOTAL	/ 207

End-of-Year Test - Grade 3

Multiplication Tables and Basic Division Facts

1. Your first problem will be to fill in the complete multiplication table.
   See how much of it you can fill in twelve minutes.

×	0	1	2	3	4	5	6	7	8	9	10	11	12
0													
1													
2													
3													
4													
5													
6													
7													
8													
9													
10													
11													
12													

In problems 2 and 3, your teacher will read you multiplication and division questions. Try to answer them as quickly as possible. In each question, he/she will only wait a little while for you to answer, and if you do not say anything, your teacher will move on to the next problem. So just try your best to answer the questions as quickly as you can.

2. Multiply.

a.	b.	c.	d.
$2 \times 7 =$ _____	$7 \times 4 =$ _____	$3 \times 3 =$ _____	$7 \times 8 =$ _____
$8 \times 3 =$ _____	$5 \times 8 =$ _____	$4 \times 4 =$ _____	$6 \times 5 =$ _____
$5 \times 5 =$ _____	$3 \times 9 =$ _____	$7 \times 7 =$ _____	$8 \times 6 =$ _____
$9 \times 4 =$ _____	$5 \times 7 =$ _____	$4 \times 8 =$ _____	$6 \times 9 =$ _____

3. Divide.

a.	b.	c.	d.
$21 \div 3 =$ _____	$32 \div 4 =$ _____	$45 \div 5 =$ _____	$50 \div 5 =$ _____
$35 \div 7 =$ _____	$40 \div 8 =$ _____	$28 \div 4 =$ _____	$72 \div 9 =$ _____
$48 \div 6 =$ _____	$66 \div 6 =$ _____	$36 \div 9 =$ _____	$18 \div 6 =$ _____
$49 \div 7 =$ _____	$56 \div 8 =$ _____	$63 \div 7 =$ _____	$27 \div 9 =$ _____

Addition and Subtraction, including Word Problems

4. Add mentally.

a. $240 + 70 =$ _____	**b.** $540 + 80 =$ _____	**c.** $59 + 89 =$ _____
$99 + 50 =$ _____	$335 + 9 =$ _____	$46 + 34 =$ _____

5. Subtract mentally.

a. $100 - 67 =$ _____	**b.** $651 - 8 =$ _____	**c.** $52 - 37 =$ _____
$73 - 68 =$ _____	$54 - 9 =$ _____	$400 - 22 =$ _____

6. Subtract and then check your answers using the grid.

a.

```
  9 6 2
- 3 8 3
```

b.

```
  7 0 0 2
- 4 5 2 6
```

7. Solve.

a. $82 + 5539 + 1254 + 278$

b. $535 + (430 - 173)$

8. Solve what number goes in place of the triangle.

a. $414 + $  $= 708$

 is _____

b. 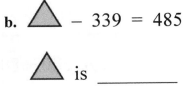 $- 339 = 485$

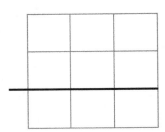 is _____

Solve.

9. Joe bought a mobile phone for $185 and a phone case for $32.
   What was his change from $300?

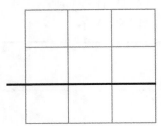   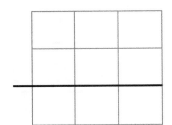

10. A family is driving 300 kilometres from their hometown to Grandmother's house.
    Ten kilometres before the half-way point they stopped to have lunch.
    How many kilometres do they still have to go?

11. A store received 100 boxes. Each box contained 8 light bulbs.

   a. How many light bulbs did the store receive?

   b. After selling 8 boxes, how many bulbs are left?

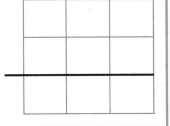

12. Draw a picture to illustrate
    the multiplication $3 \times 4 = 12$.

13. Solve: $5 \times 25 =$ _____

14. Solve.

a. $24 + 8 \times 3$	b. $2 + (5 + 4) \times 2$	c. $66 - 5 \times 5$

15. Write a multiplication sentence (NOT just the answer) to solve how many legs these
    animals have in total.

    a. seven horses _____

    b. five ducks _____

    c. eight horses and six ducks _____

16. Each table in a restaurant seats four people. How many
    tables do you need to reserve for a group of 31 people?

17. A toy store had a bag of balloons for $8
    and a toy car for $6.
    How much would it cost to buy three
    bags of balloons and three toy cars?

18. Annie is bagging hair barrettes she made. She puts four barrettes in each bag.
    She has 28 barrettes to bag. How many bags will she need?

Time

19. Write the time the clock shows, and the time 10 minutes later.

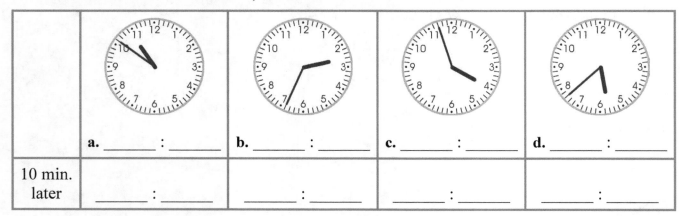

	a. _____ : _____	**b.** _____ : _____	**c.** _____ : _____	**d.** _____ : _____
10 min. later	_____ : _____	_____ : _____	_____ : _____	_____ : _____

20. **a.** The TV show starts at 6:25 PM and ends at 7:00 PM. How long is it?

   b. Mr. Mayer's plane landed at 11:30 AM. If the flight lasted for 6 hours, when did it take off?

   c. The soccer match was scheduled for 21 May, but it was postponed (delayed) by one week. What was the new date for the match?

Graphs

21. The graph shows some people's working hours on Uncle Ted's apple farm.

   a. How many hours did Erica work?

   b. How many hours did Kathy work?

   c. How many more hours did Jason work than Jack?

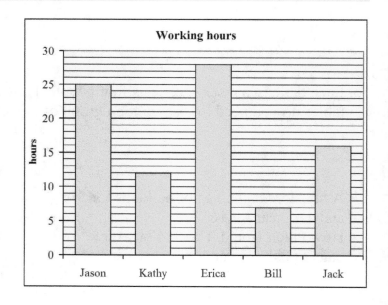

   d. How many hours did the three boys work in total?

22. Find the total cost of buying the items listed. Line up the numbers carefully when you add.

$6.60	$8.95	$1.25	$16.59

a. a calculator and a bag	**b.** two pens and a book	**c.** three pens and a calculator

23. Work out the change.

a. A book costs $7.10. You give $10. Change: $_____	**b.** A basket costs $4.45. You give $5. Change: $_____

24. A pencil case costs $2.35. If Mark buys four
of them with his $10, what will his change be?

Place Value and Rounding

25. Fill in the missing part.

a. $2000 + 60 +$ _____ $= 2760$	**b.** $700 + 20 +$ _____ $+ 9 = 2729$

26. Compare and write $<$, $>$ or $=$.

a. $6034 \ \square \ 3064$	**b.** $5156 \ \square \ 5516$	**c.** $9079 \ \square \ 9097$
d. $6000 + 3 + 40 \ \square \ 400 + 60 + 3000$		**e.** $900 + 7000 \ \square \ 90 + 7000 + 2$

27. Add and subtract.

a. $5400 + 300 =$ _____ $7800 + 800 =$ _____	**b.** $2900 - 1700 =$ _____ $8100 - 300 =$ _____

28. Round the numbers to the nearest <u>TEN</u>.

a. $743 \approx$ _____	**b.** $987 \approx$ _____	**c.** $251 \approx$ _____	**d.** $665 \approx$ _____

29. Estimate these calculations by rounding the numbers to the nearest <u>hundred</u>.
    Also, calculate the exact answer.

a. Round the numbers, then add: $3782 \qquad + \qquad 2255$ $\downarrow \qquad\qquad\qquad \downarrow$ $+$ $=$ _____	**Calculate exactly:** $\begin{array}{r} 3\ 7\ 8\ 2 \\ +\ 2\ 2\ 5\ 5 \\ \hline \end{array}$
b. Round the numbers, then subtract: $8149 \qquad - \qquad 888$ $\downarrow \qquad\qquad\qquad \downarrow$ $-$ $=$ _____	**Calculate exactly:** $\begin{array}{r} 8\ 1\ 4\ 9 \\ -\ \ \ 8\ 8\ 8 \\ \hline \end{array}$

Geometry

30. Name any special quadrilaterals.

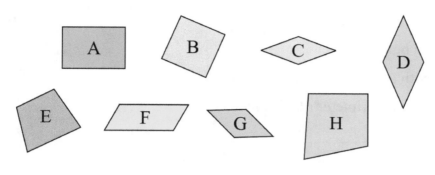

_____

_____

_____

_____

_____

_____

31. Find the perimeter and area of this shape.

Perimeter: _____

Area : _____

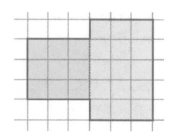

32. The picture shows a two-part lawn.

   a. Find the areas of part 1 and part 2.

   _____ and _____

   b. Find the perimeter of the whole lawn.

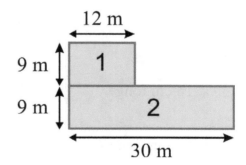

33. The perimeter of a rectangle measures 66 cm. Find the other side length, if one side measures 10 cm.

34. Draw in the grid below:

   a. a rectangle with an area of 15 square units

   b. a rectangle with a perimeter of 10 units.

35. Write a number sentence for the total area, thinking of one rectangle or two.

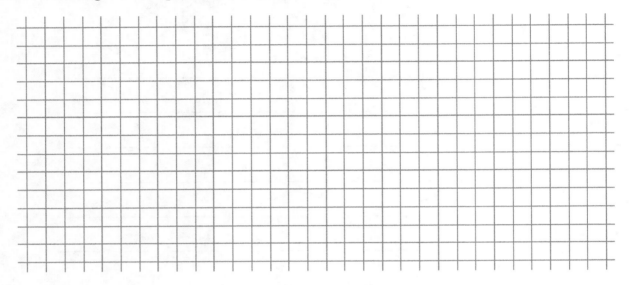

___ × (___ + ___) = ___ × ___ + ___ × ___ = _____

area of the whole rectangle   area of the first part   area of the second part

Measuring

36. Draw lines:

   a. 16 cm long

   b. 75 mm long

37. Write in order from smallest to biggest unit: cm km m mm

38. Name a unit that you can use to measure a small
    amount of water in a drinking glass.

39. Fill in the blanks with suitable units of length. Sometimes several different units
    are possible.

    a. The mountain is 2000 _____ high.   **b.** The pencil is 14 _____ long.

    c. Jeremy bought 5 _____ of potatoes.   **d.** The glass holds 300 _____ of liquid.

    e. The teacher weighs 68 _____ .   **f.** The room was 7 _____ wide.

Division and Related Concepts

40. Write two multiplications and two divisions for the same picture.

_____ × _____ = _____   _____ ÷ _____ = _____

_____ × _____ = _____   _____ ÷ _____ = _____

41. Divide, but CROSS OUT all the problems that are impossible!

a. $17 \div 1 =$ _____	**b.** $17 \div 17 =$ _____	**c.** $1 \div 1 =$ _____
$17 \div 0 =$ _____	$0 \div 0 =$ _____	$0 \div 1 =$ _____

42. Divide.

    a. $17 \div 2 =$ _____ , R _____   **b.** $24 \div 5 =$ _____ , R _____   **c.** $47 \div 7 =$ _____ , R _____

43. A team leader divided a group of 24 children into teams.
    Can he divide the children equally into teams of 5?

    Teams of 6?

    Teams of 7?

44. Annie, Rob, and Ted decided to buy a gift that cost $16 and flowers that cost $14 for
    Mom. The children shared the total cost equally. How much did each child pay?

Fractions

45. Write the fraction or mixed number.

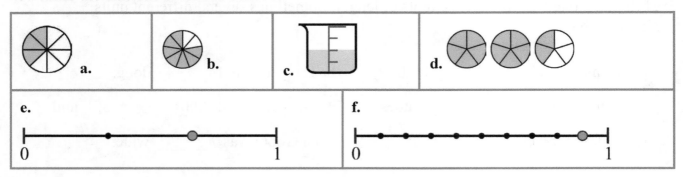

46. Write the whole numbers as fractions.

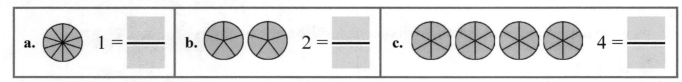

47. Mark the equivalent fractions $\frac{3}{6}$ and $\frac{1}{2}$ on the number lines.

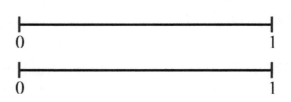

48. Shade parts for the first fraction. Shade the same *amount* in the second picture, forming an equivalent fraction. Write the second fraction.

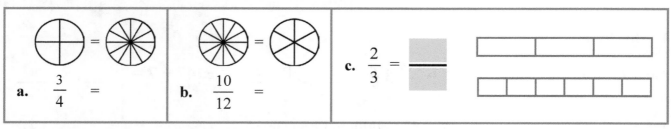

a. $\frac{3}{4} =$ b. $\frac{10}{12} =$ c. $\frac{2}{3} = \dfrac{}{}$

49. Compare the fractions.

a. $\frac{2}{7} \square \frac{2}{3}$ b. $\frac{5}{11} \square \frac{7}{11}$ c. $\frac{1}{2} \square \frac{9}{10}$ d. $\frac{1}{7} \square \frac{1}{8}$

50. Mary ate 1/2 of a strawberry pie, and David ate 7/12 of a blueberry pie.
Look at the pictures.
Who ate more pie?

Mary's pie: David's pie:

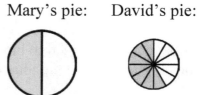

USING THE CUMULATIVE REVIEWS

The cumulative reviews include problems from various chapters of the Math Mammoth complete curriculum, up to the chapter named in the review. For example, a cumulative review for chapters 1-6 may include problems from chapters 1, 2, 3, 4, 5, and 6. The review for chapters 1-6 can be used any time after the student has gone through chapter 6.

These reviews provide additional practice and review. The teacher should decide when and if they are used -- the student does not necessarily have to complete all the reviews

I recommend using at least 2 or 3 of these reviews during the school year. The teacher can also use the reviews as diagnostic tests to find out what areas and topics the student has trouble with.

Math Mammoth complete curriculum also comes with an easy worksheet maker, which is the perfect tool to make lots of problems of a specific type, especially when it comes to calculation skills.

You can access the worksheet maker online at

https://www.mathmammoth.com/private/Make_extra_worksheets_grade3.htm

Please note that while the worksheet maker covers a lot of topics, it does not include worksheets for all the topics in the curriculum. Most notably, it does not make worksheets for word problems. However, most people find it to be a very helpful addition to the curriculum.

Cumulative Review, Grade 3, Chapters 1-2

1. Add and subtract mentally.

| a. $566 + 8 =$ | b. $730 + 80 =$ | c. $991 - 8 =$ |

2. Write the numbers as Roman numerals.

a. 25   **b.** 19   **c.** 57   **d.** 143

3. Calculate.

a. $35 - 14 - 7 + 3 = $ _____	d. $(250 - 20) + (80 - 30) = $ _____
b. $35 - (14 - 7) + 3 = $ _____	e. $250 - (20 + 80 - 30) = $ _____
c. $35 - (14 - 8 + 3) = $ _____	f. $250 - 20 + (80 - 30) = $ _____

4. Jane has a tea set with 14 cups and a tea set with 13 cups.
   She wants to invite the girls from her class for a tea party. There
   are 30 girls in her class. How many more cups does she need?

5. Multiply.

a. $3 \times 3 = $ ____	b. $5 \times 2 = $ ____	c. $3 \times 30 = $ ____	d. $0 \times 9 = $ ____
$4 \times 2 = $ ____	$3 \times 6 = $ ____	$4 \times 20 = $ ____	$10 \times 0 = $ ____
$0 \times 8 = $ ____	$4 \times 8 = $ ____	$2 \times 400 = $ ____	$22 \times 1 = $ ____

6. First write the multiplications as additions. Then solve.

   a. 2×20

   b. 3×50

7. Write a number sentence or sentences for each problem and solve them.

a. Ted has three rolls of string with 6 metres on each roll.
What is the total length of the string on the three rolls?

b. Jane has 16 golf balls and 8 tennis balls. She put the balls into bags with four in each bag. How many bags does she need?

8. Write one addition and one subtraction sentence to match the model.

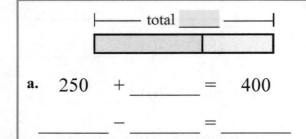

a.   250   +_____   =   400

_____ – _____ = _____

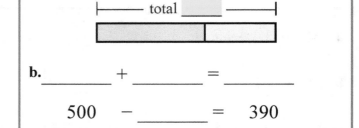

b. _____ + _____ = _____

500   – _____   =   390

9. Subtract.

a.   8 8 8   **b.**   4 5 0   **c.**   6 0 2   **d.**   8 0 0
       – 2 9 9   – 1 3 4   – 3 4 4   – 6 5 7

10. Can you buy three dolls for $48 each and pay with $150?
If yes, how much money will you have left?
If no, how much more money would you need?

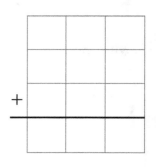

11. Estimate the total costs using rounded numbers.

a. Rent, $556 and groceries for $387	**b.** An adult's movie ticket for $58 and a child's movie ticket for $38
Rent, about $_____	Adult's ticket, about $_____
Groceries, about $_____	Child's ticket, about $_____
Total, about $_____	Total cost, about $_____

Cumulative Review, Grade 3, Chapters 1 - 3

1. Jim drove from Toronto to Montreal in two days, driving the
   same distance each day. How many kilometres did he drive each day?

	Barrie	Kingston	Montreal	Ottawa	Quebec City
Kingston	341				
Montreal	620	287			
Ottawa	412	195	198		
Quebec City	875	542	254	449	
Toronto	110	262	540	402	796

2. Ben and Joe went on a trip:

   (1) They took a bus from Barrie to Toronto.

   (2) A friend took them from Toronto to Ottawa.

   (3) Then they travelled from Ottawa to
       Quebec City on a bus.

   What was the total number of kilometres they travelled?

   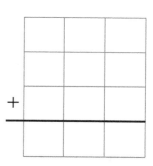

3. Three parts make up one whole. Write an addition and a subtraction sentence, and solve.

   |—— total 698 ——|
   | ? | 196 | 153 |

   a. _____ + _____ + _____ = _____

      _____ − _____ − _____ = _____

   |—— total 450 ——|
   | 125 | 250 | ? |

   b. _____ + _____ + _____ = _____

      _____ − _____ − _____ = _____

4. Solve the problems.

a. A math teacher bought four rulers that cost $2 each, and ten note pads that cost $3 each. What was the total cost?

b. Sue and her friend shared equally the taxi fare to the mall, which was $50. At the mall, Sue bought a snack for $5. How much did Sue spend for the taxi fare plus the snack?

5. Write the Roman numerals using normal numbers.

a. IX   **b.** CXXI   **c.** LXVII   **d.** XIV

6. Write multiplication sentences for the jumps on the number lines below.

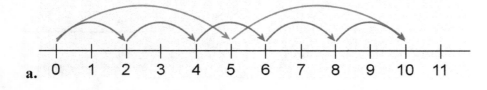

a.

_____ × _____ = _____

_____ × _____ = _____

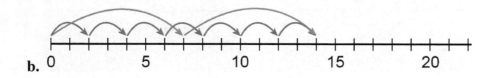

b.

_____ × _____ = _____

_____ × _____ = _____

7. Some scientists were studying giraffes in a park in Africa. The pictograph shows how many giraffes they saw at a waterhole each week. One  means 15 giraffes.

a. How many giraffes did they see in week 27?

b. How many more giraffes did they see in week 27 than in week 28?

Week 25	🦒🦒🦒🦒
Week 26	🦒🦒🦒🦒🦒🦒
Week 27	🦒🦒🦒🦒🦒🦒🦒
Week 28	🦒🦒🦒

Cumulative Review, Grade 3, Chapters 1 - 4

1. For each problem, write a companion subtraction or addition sentence, and solve.

a. _____ + 120 = 770	**b.** _____ + _____ = _____
_____ − _____ = _____	_____ − 9 = 633

2. Reading the list of numbers below from left to right,

    a. add the first and second numbers;

    b. subtract the fourth number from the ninth number;

    c. add the eighth number to the tenth number and
       then subtract the fifth number.

12,   14,   21,   33,   87,   32,   435,   54,   89,   100

3. Calculate.

a. $(18 - 5) - (3 + 6) =$ _____	**b.** $(300 - 50) - (80 - 30) =$ _____
$18 - 5 - 3 + 6 =$ _____	$300 - 50 - 80 - 30 =$ _____

4. Solve the problems.

a. Karen baked 30 cupcakes. She ate one. Her brother took two. Then her mother said she
    needed 2 cupcakes for herself and each of the twelve ladies coming for afternoon tea.

Are there enough cupcakes left?

If not, how many more cupcakes
does Karen need to make?

b. The teacher gave each of the nine children 12 marbles to play a math game.
    After the class, only 99 marbles were turned back in.
    How many marbles were lost?

5. Write the time using the hours : minutes way.

a. 8 past 6	b. 12 to 7	c. 29 past 3	d. 33 past 5
_____ : _____	_____ : _____	___ : _____	_____ : _____
e. 24 to 5	f. 21 to 6	g. 2 to 12	h. 17 to 1
_____ : _____	_____ : _____	_____ : _____	_____ : _____

6. Calculate.

a. $8 \times 10 - 2 + 5 =$ _____	b. $6 + 7 \times (4 - 2) =$ _____
c. $3 \times 4 - 2 \times 3 =$ _____	d. $2 \times (4 + 4) \times 2 =$ _____

7. Continue the patterns:

a. $564 - 5 =$ _____

$564 - 10 =$ _____

$564 - 15 =$ _____

$564 -$ ____ $=$ _____

$564 -$ ____ $=$ _____

$564 -$ ____ $=$ _____

b. $888 + 12 =$ _____

$886 + 14 =$ _____

$884 + 16 =$ _____

_____ $+$ ____ $=$ _____

_____ $+$ ____ $=$ _____

_____ $+$ ____ $=$ _____

8. Solve the problems.

a. Bonnie stayed at the beach for three weeks. Then she
went to her grandparents' farm for two more weeks.
How many days did she spend at the beach and the farm
in total?

b. Benjamin can walk to school in fifteen minutes. From Monday through Friday,
how many minutes does he spend walking to and from school?

Cumulative Review, Grade 3, Chapters 1 - 5

1. Add mentally.

| a. $49 + 13 =$ _____ | b. $46 + 15 =$ _____ | c. $25 + 39 =$ _____ |

2. Subtract in parts: break the second number into tens and ones.

a.	b.	c.
$98 - \underline{66}$	$54 - \underline{26}$	$73 - \underline{17}$
$98 - \underline{60} - \underline{6} =$ _____	$54 - \underline{} - \underline{} =$ _____	$73 - \underline{} - \underline{} =$ _____

3. Write $<$, $>$ or $=$.

   a. $350 - 18$ ☐ $350 - 15$ b. $180 - 15$ ☐ $190 - 25$

   c. $264 + 7$ ☐ $267 + 8$ d. $62 - 27$ ☐ $61 - 27$

4. Potatoes are \$4 per kilogram. If you buy three kilograms, and pay with \$20, what is your change?

5. Mary spent three weeks in Cairns, two weeks in Townsville, and nineteen days in Mackay. How many days did she spend altogether in the three places?

6. Subtract. Check your answers.

| a. $\begin{array}{r} 9\ 0\ 4 \\ -\ 3\ 2\ 7 \\ \hline \end{array}$ $+$ _____ | b. $\begin{array}{r} 8\ 1\ 2 \\ -\ 3\ 2\ 7 \\ \hline \end{array}$ $+$ _____ |

7. Erica made refrigerator magnets and sold them at the flea market last Saturday.

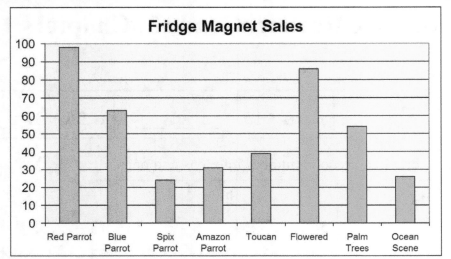

a. Read the graph, and tell <u>about</u> how many parrot magnets she sold in total (red parrot, blue parrot, Spix parrot, and Amazon parrot magnets).

b. <u>About</u> how many other kinds of magnets did she sell (not parrot magnets)?

8. Calculate in the correct order.

a. $7 + 4 \times 7$	**b.** $30 + 6 \times (6 - 6)$	**c.** $2 \times 44 - 8 \times 0$

9. How much time passes?

a. From 2:26 to 10:18	**b.** From 8:29 to 12:02	**c.** From 2:56 to 5:34

10. Write as dollar amounts.

four nickels and a dime	three quarters, one dime, and three nickels	two nickels, two dimes, and one 50-cent piece
a. $_____	**b.** $_____	**c.** $_____

Cumulative Review, Grade 3, Chapters 1 - 6

1. Find the missing factors.

a. _____ × 4 = 16 _____ × 8 = 64	b. _____ × 9 = 0 _____ × 3 = 27	c. _____ × 6 = 36 _____ × 4 = 36	d. _____ × 5 = 45 _____ × 2 = 18

2. Write using Roman numerals.

a. 15	b. 32	c. 47	d. 56

3. Write the time using the expressions "to" and "past".

    a. 6:38   b. 3:56

    c. 2:12   d. 7:43

4. Sylvia started exercising with an exercise video at 7:55 PM,
   and it ended 30 minutes later. At what time did it end?
   Use your practice clock to help.

5. Estimate these calculations by rounding the numbers to the nearest hundred.
   On the right, calculate the exact answer.

a. Estimate:	Calculate exactly:
7738 + 2022 ↓ ↓ + = _____	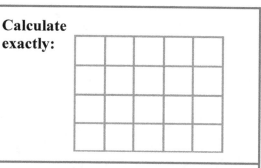
b. Estimate: 9152 − 4728 ↓ ↓ − = _____	Calculate exactly: 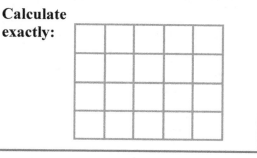

6. Fill in the table.

a. Two thousand and two				**b.** One thousand and fifteen				**c.** Five thousand nine hundred and six			
thou-sands	hund-reds	tens	ones	thou-sands	hund-reds	tens	ones	thou-sands	hund-reds	tens	ones

7. Write an addition or subtraction using an unknown, such as ? or some symbol. Solve.

a. Helen has saved $25. She wants to buy a book for $29.
How much more does she still need to save?

b. Annie bought a gift for her mom for $29, and now she has $16 left.
How much money did Annie have before buying the gift?

8. Solve.

a. Sandra bought groundnuts for $8.65,
liquorice for $5.00 and a dozen eggs for $2.95.
Calculate the total cost.

b. Find the cost of three schoolbags
if one schoolbag costs $87.

Also, estimate the answer using rounded
numbers.

My estimate: _____

+

Cumulative Review, Grade 3, Chapters 1 - 7

1. Write the following numbers in Roman Numerals.

a. 16	b. 88	c. 149	d. 219

2. Multiply.

a.	b.	c.	d.
$5 \times 5 =$ _____	$2 \times 11 =$ _____	$2 \times 7 =$ _____	$5 \times 3 =$ _____
$12 \times 12 =$ _____	$8 \times 6 =$ _____	$4 \times 12 =$ _____	$1 \times 10 =$ _____
$7 \times 5 =$ _____	$3 \times 11 =$ _____	$6 \times 7 =$ _____	$8 \times 8 =$ _____

3. Barbra bought two dolls for $10.35 each and two teddy bears for $13.90 each.

   a. Find the total cost.

   b. She paid with $50.
     How much was her change?

4. Round these numbers to the nearest hundred.

a.	b.	c.
$8539 \approx$ _____	$9687 \approx$ _____	$5323 \approx$ _____
$3551 \approx$ _____	$1621 \approx$ _____	$2399 \approx$ _____

5. Solve (find the number that the symbol stands for).

a. $1500 + \triangle = 2100$	b. $5200 - \triangle = 4700$	c. $\triangle - 2300 = 2300$
$\triangle =$ _____	$\triangle =$ _____	$\triangle =$ _____

6. Write the time the clock shows. Below, write the time using "past" and "to."

a. _____ : _____	**b.** _____ : _____	**c.** _____ : _____

7. Which operations will make the number sentences true?

a. 14 ☐ (1 ☐ 12) = 26	**c.** 20 ☐ 4 ☐ 8 = 88
b. 90 ☐ 5 ☐ 4 ☐ 4 = 69	**d.** 10 ☐ (2 ☐ 4) ☐ 5 = 55

8. Patty got up at 5:19 and spent 3 minutes brushing her teeth,
   13 minutes showering and dressing and 18 minutes eating
   breakfast. Then, she left for work.
   What time did she leave for work?

9. Work out change: find the missing money amount.

a. $1.70 + _____ = $5	**b.** $2.30 + _____ = $3	**c.** $4.70 + _____ = $20
95c + _____ = $5	$3.45 + _____ = $10	$14.10 + _____ = $50

10. Some children are watching videos. Write the ending time when the starting time and the
    length of the video are given.

a.	b.	c.
6:25 → _____ : _____	1:03 → _____ : _____	12:05 → _____ : _____
33 minutes	28 minutes	42 minutes

Cumulative Review, Grade 3, Chapters 1 - 8

1. Write an addition and a subtraction to match the bar model. Fill in the missing parts.

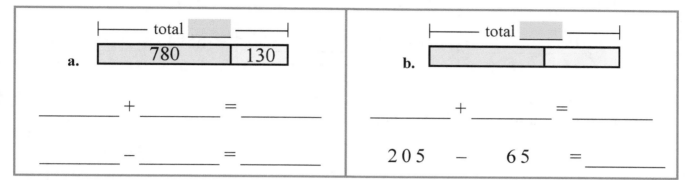

a.

_____ + _____ = _____

_____ − _____ = _____

b.

_____ + _____ = _____

2 0 5 − 6 5 = _____

2. Subtract. Check your answers.

a.
$$\begin{array}{r} 7\ 9\ 0\ 4 \\ -\ 3\ 2\ 9\ 7 \end{array}$$ + _____

b.
$$\begin{array}{r} 5\ 0\ 1\ 2 \\ -\ \ \ 3\ 2\ 7 \end{array}$$ + _____

3. Tina needs three whole weeks to write a report. If she starts
   writing on November 3, when will she finish writing?

4. Compare. Write $<$, $>$ or $=$ in the box.

a. 9018 ☐ 9180

b. $5000 + 600$ ☐ $500 + 6000$

c. 2387 ☐ 2378

d. $8000 + 50 + 2$ ☐ $200 + 5000 + 800$

5. Solve.

a. $10 \times 25 =$	b. $8 \times 90 =$	c. $70 \times 4 =$
d. $120 + 5 \times 7 =$	e. $12 \times 9 + 20 =$	f. $(11 - 3) \times 3 + 5 =$

6. Underline the greatest number in each box. Round all the numbers to the nearest thousand.

a. 8509 ≈ _____	**b.** 3899 ≈ _____	**c.** 5549 ≈ _____
5479 ≈ _____	3809 ≈ _____	5459 ≈ _____
7330 ≈ _____	3890 ≈ _____	5594 ≈ _____

7. In the grid on the right, draw a rectangle that is three units by four units. Then find its perimeter and area.

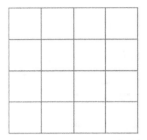

Perimeter: _____

Area: _____

8. Write a number sentence for the total area first, and then for each part..

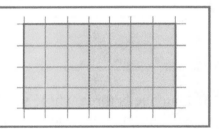

____ × (____ + ____) = ____ × ____ + ____ × ____

area of the   area of the   area of the
whole rectangle   first part   second part

9. Now it is your turn to draw the rectangle. Fill in the blanks.

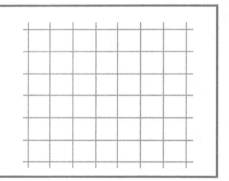

3 × (1 + 5) = ____ × ____ + ____ × ____

area of the   area of the   area of the
whole rectangle   first part   second part

10. Write the names of these three-dimensional figures, or *solids*:

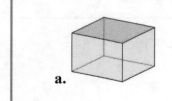 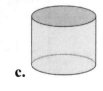 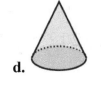

a. _____

b. _____

c. _____

d. _____

Cumulative Review, Grade 3, Chapters 1 - 9

1. Solve (find the number that the symbol stands for).

a. $\triangle + 11 = 349$ $\triangle = $ _____	b. $530 - \triangle = 320$ $\triangle = $ _____	c. $\triangle - 1600 = 500$ $\triangle = $ _____

2. Write an addition or subtraction using an unknown, such as ? or some symbol. Solve.

a. The perimeter of a rectangle is 30 m. Its one side is 6 m. How long is the other side?
b. Mom had $200 when she went shopping. She came home with $78. How much did she spend?

3. Write the numbers using Roman numerals.

a. 124	b. 40	c. 90	d. 222

4. Robert is building a clubhouse and the floor will be two by three metres.

   a. What will the area of the floor be?

   b. What will the perimeter of the floor be?

5. Multiply.

a.	b.	c.	d.
$9 \times 5 = $ _____	$11 \times 12 = $ _____	$9 \times 9 = $ _____	$8 \times 7 = $ _____
$6 \times 5 = $ _____	$9 \times 12 = $ _____	$7 \times 9 = $ _____	$4 \times 7 = $ _____
$8 \times 5 = $ _____	$12 \times 12 = $ _____	$6 \times 9 = $ _____	$7 \times 7 = $ _____

6. Write a number sentence for the total area, thinking of one rectangle or two.

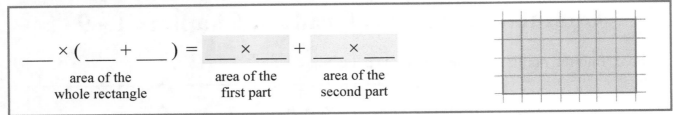

___ × (___ + ___) = ___ × ___ + ___ × ___

area of the whole rectangle   area of the first part   area of the second part

7. Write the cent amounts as dollar amounts, and vice versa.

a. _____c = $4.65   **b.** 5c = $_____   **c.** _____c = $2.05

8. Write the weight using kilograms and grams.

a. _____ kg _____ g   **b.** _____kg _____ g   **c.** _____kg _____ g

9. Solve the problems.

a. Susan has three favourite cookie recipes. The first recipe makes 5 dozen cookies, the second recipe makes 4 dozen and the third recipe makes 2 dozen. How many cookies will Susan have if she makes all three recipes?

b. Jack bought nine pairs of socks for $2 each, a shirt for $18, and pants for $27. What was the total cost?

c. Henry has two quarters, three dimes and four nickels. He traded them to Bob for one coin. What was the coin?

Cumulative Review, Grade 3, Chapters 1 - 10

1. Write the fact families.

a.	b.	c.
_____ × 2 = 14	_____ × _____ = _____	_____ × _____ = _____
_____ × _____ = _____	_____ × _____ = _____	_____ × _____ = _____
_____ ÷ 2 = _____	35 ÷ _____ = 7	42 ÷ 6 = _____
_____ ÷ _____ = _____	_____ ÷ _____ = _____	_____ ÷ _____ = _____

2. Solve.

a. Alice is bagging apples with 4 apples in each bag.
   She has 12 bags to fill. How many apples will she need?

b. Sally had a piece of material that was 36 centimetres long.
   She cut it into three equal pieces. How long is each piece?

c. How much money do you have if you have four quarters,
   three dimes and four nickels?

d. Write a word problem that will be solved with the division $24 \div 6 =$ _____

3. Find the missing numbers.

a. $40 \div$ ____ $= 8$	**b.** _____ $\div 5 = 7$	**c.** $4 \times$ ____ $= 48$	**d.** $4 \times 7 =$ _____
$72 \div$ ____ $= 8$	_____ $\div 6 = 7$	$8 \times$ ____ $= 48$	$8 \times 8 =$ _____

4. Solve.

a. $7 \div 2 =$ _____ R _____	**b.** $13 \div 5 =$ _____ R _____	**c.** $21 \div 2 =$ _____ R _____
$9 \div 2 =$ _____ R _____	$14 \div 5 =$ _____ R _____	$47 \div 6 =$ _____ R _____

5. **a.** What measuring unit can you use to measure the weight of light items, such as an apple or a notebook?

  b. What measuring unit can you use to measure the weight of heavy items, such as a refrigerator or a car?

  c. What measuring units can you use to measure the length of a room?

  d. What measuring units can you use to measure the height of a mountain?

6. The picture shows Amanda's garden. She is going to plant potatoes in the smaller part, and different vegetables in the bigger part.

  a. Calculate the area that will be used for potatoes.

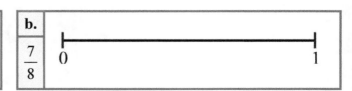

  b. Find the total area of her garden.

  c. Find the perimeter of the whole garden.

7. Mark the fractions on the number lines.

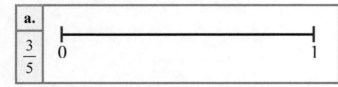

Printed in the USA
CPSIA information can be obtained
at www.ICGtesting.com
LVHW080743200224
772265LV00010B/224